THE BIG BOOK OF
TONGUE
TW...S
&... E
TA...

ILLUSTRA... AND

...OLD

Aa

Andrew Airpump ask'd his Aunt
    her Ailment:
Did Andrew Airpump ask his Aunt
    her Ailment?
If Andrew Airpump ask'd his Aunt
    her Ailment,
Where was the Ailment of Andrew
    Airpump's Aunt?

Bb

Billy Button bought a Butter'd
    Biscuit:
Did Billy Button buy a Butter'd
    Biscuit?
If Billy Button bought a Butter'd
    Biscuit,
Where's the Butter'd Biscuit Billy
    Button bought?

Ee

Enoch Elkrig ate an empty
    Eggshell;
Did Enoch Elkrig eat an empty
    Eggshell?
If Enoch Elkrig ate an empty
    Eggshell,
Where's the empty Eggshell
    Enoch Elkrig ate?

Ff

Fran... Fribble figured on a
    ...man's Filly:
Did ... is Fribble figure ...
    ...hman's Filly?
If ... e ribble figured ...
    ...chman... ...
Whe... he Frenchman's ...
    rancis Fribble figured on?

Ii

Inigo Impey itch'd for an
    Indian Image:
Did Inigo Impey itch for an
    Indian Image?
If Inigo Impey itch'd for an
    Indian Image,
Where's the Indian Image Inigo
    Impey itch'd for?

Jj

Jumping Jackey jeer'd a Jesting
    Juggler;
Did Jumping Jackey jeer a Jesting
    Juggler?
If Jumping Jackey jeer'd a
    Jesting Juggler,
Where's the Jesting Juggler
    Jumping Jackey jeered?

Cc

Crazy Craycroft caught a Crate of
    crickl'd Crabs:
Did Crazy Craycroft catch a Crate
    of crickl'd Crabs?
If Crazy Craycroft caught a Crate
    of crickled Crabs,
Where's the Crate of crickl'd Crabs
    Crazy Craycroft caught?

Dd

Davy Dolldrum dream'd he drove
    a Dragon:
Did Davy Dolldrum dream he drove
    a Dragon?
If Davy Dolldrum dream'd he drove
    a Dragon,
Where's the Dragon Davy Dolldrum
    dream'd he drove?

Gg

Gaffer Gilpin grabbed a Goose
    and Gander:
Did Gaffer Gilpin grab a Goose
    and Gander?
If Gaffer Gilpin grabbed a Goose
    and Gander,
Where's the Goose and Gander
    Gaffer Gilpin grabbed?

Hh

Humphrey Hunchback had a
    Hundred Hedgehogs:
Did Humphrey Hunchback have a
    Hundred Hedgehogs?
If Humphrey Hunchback had a
    Hundred Hedgehogs,
Where's the Hundred Hedgehogs
    Humphrey Hunchback had?

Kk

Kimbo Kemble kick'd his Kinsman's
    Kettle:
Did Kimbo Kemble kick his
    Kinsman's Kettle?
If Kimbo Kemble kick'd his
    Kinsman's Kettle,
Where's the Kinsman's Kettle
    Kimbo Kemble kick'd?

Ll

Lanky Lawrence lost his Lass
    and Lobster:
Did Lanky Lawrence lose his Lass
    and Lobster?
If Lanky Lawrence lost his Lass
    and Lobster,
Where's the Lass and Lobster
    Lanky Lawrence lost?

To Francis

*"...after I passed the last grass plant
of Sassafras fast, alas."*

THE BIG BOOK OF
TONGUE TWISTERS & DOUBLE TALK

COLLECTED AND ILLUSTRATED BY ARNOLD ARNOLD

RANDOM HOUSE • NEW YORK

THE BIG BOOK OF TONGUE TWISTERS AND DOUBLE TALK COLLECTED AND ILLUSTRATED BY ARNOLD ARNOLD

ACKNOWLEDGMENTS:
"Burgess' Unabridged Dictionary" from *Burgess Unabridged* by Gelett Burgess, J. B. Lippincott Company, 1914; reprinted by permission of the estate of Gelett Burgess.
"Watchers of the Night" from "Watchers of the Night" by James Thurber, *The New Yorker*, December 26, 1959; reprinted by permission of Helen Thurber.
"Pythagorean Razzle-Dazzle," "Circuit Breaker," and "Riot Diet" by Sid Gary, quoted by permission of the author.

Peter Piper's Prolix Preface:

"Peter Piper,
without Pretensions to Precocity
or Profoundness,
Puts Pen to Paper to Produce
these Puzzling Pages,
Purposely to Please the Palates
of Pretty Prattling Playfellows,
Proudly Presuming that with Proper Penetration
it will Probably, and Perhaps Positively,
Prove a Peculiarly Pleasant
and Profitable Path to Proper,
Plain and Precise Pronunciation.

He Prays Parents to Purchase
this Playful Performance,
Partly to Pay him for his Patience and Pains;
Partly to Provide for the Profit
of the Printers and Publishers;
but Principally to Prevent
the Pernicious Prevalence
of Perverse Pronunciation."

1

Crumbs

I'd rather be rooked by crooked cooks
than choke on crumby cookies
baked by ruthless cooks,
too lazy to look at cookbooks.

The Tooting Tudor Tutor

A Tudor who tooted the flute
Tried to tutor two tooters to toot.
Said the two to their tutor:
Is it tougher to toot, or
To tutor two tooters to toot?

The sixth sheik's sixth sheep's sick.

Bitty Botty Bat Some Putty

Betty Botter bought some butter.
"But," she said, "the butter's bitter;
if I put it in my batter,
it will make my batter bitter.
But a bit of better butter,
that would make my batter better."

So she bought a bit of butter,
better than her bitter butter,
and she put it in her batter,
and the batter was not bitter.
So t'was better Betty Botter
bought a bit of better butter.

Toddler Twaddle

Mud'll befuddle muddled toddlers
    who paddle in puddles.
If swaddled and cuddled,
    they'll cackle and prattle.
But tickle their middles,
    they'll snicker and giggle.
Befuddled, tickled and
    cuddled toddlers aren't subtle.

Virtue Rewarded

A famous fish-factor found himself
father of five flirting females—
Fanny, Florence, Fernanda, Francesca, and Fenella.
The first four were freckle-faced frumps,
fretful, flippant, foolish and flaunting.
Fenella was fine-featured, fresh,
fleet-footed, frank, free, and full of fun.
The fisher failed, and was forced by fickle fortune
to forfeit his forefathers' fine fields,
and find a forlorn farmhouse in a forsaken forest.
The four fretful females, fond of feasts in feathers
and fashionable finery, fumed at their fugitive father.

Forsaken by fulsome, flattering fortune-hunters
who followed them when first they flourished,
Fenella fondled her father, flavored their food,
and forgot her flattering followers.
The father found himself forced to forage
in foreign parts for a fortune for his five fondlings.
The first four were fain to foster their frivolity
with fine frills and fans, fit to finish their father's finances;
Fenella, fearful of flooring him,
formed a fancy for full fresh flowers.
Fate favored the fish-factor for a few days,
but in a fog his faithful Filley's footsteps faltered.
In front of a fortified forsaken fortress, forlorn
and feeble from fasting, he fell full flat on the floor.
Fresh in the forenoon, he forthwith flew to the fruitful fields,
and not forgetting Fenella, he filched a fair flower;
when a foul, frightening, fiendish figure flashed forth:
"Felonious fellow, fingering my flowers, I'll finish you!"
Fenella, forthwith fortified by filial fondness,
followed her father and flung her faultless form
at the foot of the frightful figure, who forgave her father,
for he had fervently fallen in a fiery fit of love
for the fair Fenella.
He feasted her till, fascinated by his faithfulness,
she forgot the ferocity of his face, form and features,
and frankly and fondly fixed Friday,
the fifth of February, for their wedding day.
There was festivity, fragrance, finery, fireworks, fritters,
fish, flesh, fowl, flip, and fare fit for the fastidious;
fruit, fuss, fiddlers and fifers;
and the frightful form of the fortunate and frumpish fiend
fell from him, and he fell at Fenella's feet
a fair-favored, fine, frank, freeman of the forest.
Behold the fruits of filial affection.

Shucks, Woodchuck, Chuck!

How much wood would a woodchuck chuck
if a woodchuck could chuck wood?
He would chuck, he would, as much as he could,
and chuck as much wood as a woodchuck would
if a woodchuck could chuck wood.

What a shame such a shapely sash
should such shabby stitches show.

Filamentious Conjunction

When a twister a-twisting will twist him a twist,
For the twisting of his twist, he three twines doth intwist;
But if one of the twines of the twist do untwist,
The twine that untwisteth untwisteth the twist.

Untwirling the twine that untwisteth between,
He twirls, with his twister, the two in a twine;
Then twice having twisted the twines of the twine,
He twitcheth the twice he had twined in twain.

The twain that in twining before in the twine,
As twines were intwisted he now doth untwine;
Twist the twain inter-twisting a twine more between,
He, twirling his twister, makes a twist of the twine.

Confounding Countdown

1 old Oxford ox opening oysters

2 timid toads, totally tired, trying to trot to Tarrytown

3 terrible, thumping tigers tickling trout,
   trying to train their tongues to trill

4 fat frogs fanning flickering flames, frying fritters,
   and fiddling ferociously

5 floating fishing boats frivolously full of fresh fruit
   and fiery flowers

6 sportsmen shooting snipe, sitting in slick slim
   slippery saplings

7 Severn salmon swallowing shrimp

8 Englishmen eagerly examining Europe,
   elegantly eating Easter eggs

9 nimble noblemen nibbling nuts, navigating ninety-nine miles

10 tinkers tinkling upon ten tin tinder-boxes
   with tenpenny tacks

11 elephants elegantly equipped

12 typographical topographers typically translating type

Who's Who

There was a man, and his name was Dob;
And he had a wife, and her name was Mob;
And he had a dog, and he called it Cob;
And she had a cat, called Chitterabob.

Cob, says Dob;
Chitterabob, says Mob;
Cob was Dob's dog;
Chitterabob Mob's cat.

Simpering shrimps primp. Skimpy chimps limp.
Jinxed blimps sink, but scrimping imps shrink.

That's That

Now, that is a word that may often be joined,
For that that may be doubled is clear to the mind.
And that that that is right is as plain to the view,
As that that that that we use is rightly used too.
And that that that that that line has in it is right—
In accordance with grammar—is plain in our sight.

It is true, for all that, that that that that that signifies
is not the one to which I refer.

I need not your needles, they're needless to me;
For kneading of noodles, t'were needless, you see;
But did my neat knickers but need to be kneed,
I then should have need of your needles indeed.

It Takes a Heap of Bevies

To Make a Swarm a Mob

But did you know that a flock of ships is called a fleet,
a fleet of sheep is called a flock,
a flock of girls is called a bevy,
a bevy of wolves is called a pack,
a pack of thieves is called a gang,
a gang of angels is called a host,
a host of porpoises is called a shoal,
a shoal of buffaloes is called a herd,
a herd of children is called a troop,
a troop of partridges is called a covey,
a covey of stars is called a galaxy,
a galaxy of people is called a mob,
a mob of rubbish is called a heap,
a heap of bulls is called a drove,
a drove of whales is called a school,
a school of worshippers is called a congregation,
a congregation of engineers is called a corps,
a corps of robbers is called a band,
a band of bees is called a swarm,
and a swarm of children is called a crowd?

Of all the felt I ever felt,
I never felt a piece of felt
which felt as fine as that felt felt,
when first I felt that felt hat's felt.

Stumped Skunk

A skunk sat on a stump.
The skunk thinked
the stump stunk,
but the stump thunk
the skunk stunk.

Chop shops stock chops.

Twenty-five F's

All Fume and Fret, Fuss, Fidget, Fancy, Fever, Funking, Fright,
Ferment, Fault-Fearing, Faintness—more F's yet:
Flushed, Frigid, Flurried, Flinching, Fitful, Flat,
Add Famished, Fuddled and Fatigued to that;
Funeral, Fate-Foreboding.

Astounding Sounds

Cats' scrutiny makes rats scat quickest.
Cross cats caterwaul.
Crows caw at cows
And crickets chirp in thickets.

Swan Song

Swan swam over the sea,
Swim, swan, swim!
Swan swam back again,
Well swum, swan!

14

Noble Hobby

Old oily Ollie oils old oily autos.

Though the tough cough and hiccough plough me through,
O'er life's dark lough my course I still pursue.

The Timorous Trimble

The Trimble saw the Gillybut
Careering through the sky:
"Come down," she called; "there is a Wunth
Which snaps at those who fly!"

16

The Trimble watched the Gillybut
Sail forth upon the sea.
"Put back," she wailed; "the east is red—
'T will blow a Shimmerkee!"

The Trimble found the Gillybut
Asleep beneath a wall.
"Get up," she cried; "now just suppose
The Tangskip were to fall!"

The Trimble spied the Gillybut
At supper on a bough.
"Jump off," she screamed; "you're sure to catch
Odilopasis now!"

The Trimble plagued the Gillybut
In this wise day by day;
But *who* they were and *what* she feared
It's difficult to say.

17

Fish Mish-Mash

A frolicsome, fretful flying fish
Had a frenzied, fearful dying wish
To make a meal
Of an electric eel,
But a flounder found it more fun to founder.

Watchers of the Night

'Twas throllog and the siren tones did shriek
    and gibber in the night,
All menace were the bomberdrones,
    and the mom wrath outright.

Three gray geese in a green field grazing,
Gray were the geese and green was the grazing.

Write's Right

Write we know is written right,
When we see it written write.
But when we see it written wright,
We know 'tis not then written right.
For write, to have it written right,
Must not be written right nor wright,
Nor yet should it be written rite,
But write—for so 'tis written right.

A big black bug bit a big black bear,
made the big black bear bleed blood.

Pythagorean Razzle-Dazzle

The square of the hypotenuse of the right triangle
is equal to the napid of the miffdown
of the other two sides.

Circuit Breaker

You must remember
that in this circuit the generator only operates
when the fornstaff is generated by the dreelsprail
sparking the turfenfoil.
Is that perfectly clear?

Riot Diet

Steefils on toast
Sautéed bramishawns
Korkasauce with potatoes
Kerbits and milk
Turfenfoil coffee with a blamis sandwich
Hermilberries and cream
Taffelsnords on rye bread
Snerbs with krivit mushrooms
Zilts with sauerkraut
Tankerin zoltash imported Scotch
Kerl salad with grinks dressing
Gaugnits with sweet potatoes
Frimps without potatoes
Tursin tassin dessert with heavy cream
Zwerzwings sardines with zwafel crackers
Vimilforty cheese kribbles from Holland

Give me a steak with plamits on the side
and korblit sauce fanison.

Burgess' Unabridged Dictionary

When vorianders seek to huzzlecoo,
　　When jurpid splooch or vilpours drillig bores,
When cowcats kipe, or moobles wog, or you
　　Machizzled are by yourfs or xenogores,

Remember Burgess Unabridged, and think
　　How quisty is his culpid yod and yab!
No fidgeltick, with goigsome iobink,
　　No varmic orobaldity—his gab!

No more tin tiddling slubs, like fidgelticks,
　　Rizgidgeting your speech, shall lallify;
But your jujasm, like vorgid gollohix,
　　Shall all your woxy meem golobrify!

Bripkin:	One who half does things; second hand, imitation
Drillig:	A tiresome lingerer, one who talks too long
Elp:	A tricky, sly or elusive person, a promiser
Fidgeltick:	Food that is a bore to eat
Geefoojet:	An unnecessary thing, an article seldom used
Gorm:	A human hog; to take more than one's share
Jirriwig:	A traveller who does not see the country
Oofle:	A person whose name one cannot remember; to forget
Paloodle:	To give unnecessary advice; one who thus bores
Rizgidget:	An inability to make up one's mind; an indecision
Slub:	A mild indisposition which does not incapacitate
Squinch:	To watch and wait anxiously, hoping for a lucky turn
Tashivation:	The art of answering without listening to questions
Unk:	An unwelcome, inappropriate or duplicate present
Wijjicle:	A perverse household article, always out of order
Wog:	Food on the face; unconscious adornment of the person
Yod:	A ban or restriction on pleasant things
Zobzib:	An amiable blunderer, one displaying misguided zeal

That's Our Liz, That Is

Liz is a miss who'll fizz, wheeze and sneeze,
    if squeezed, quizzed and kissed.
Gee whiz, sis, don't tease,
    squeak or shriek when tweaked.
But Liz is a slick chick who mends tweed britches
    in need of needle stitches.
She succeeds in retreading tweeds
    with speed indeed.

24

Fish Tale

A fresh young fisher named Fisher
Once fished for a fish in a fissure.
The fish with a grin
Pulled the fisherman in,
And they're fishing the fissure for Fisher.

No Pets Allowed

It's inept etiquette to take
marmosets aboard jets.
Zooming jets boom.
Soon marmosets fret.
Fretting pets wet.

I would if I could;
If I couldn't, how could I?
I couldn't, without I could, could I?
Could you, without you could, could ye?
     Could ye? Could ye?
Could you, without you could, could ye?

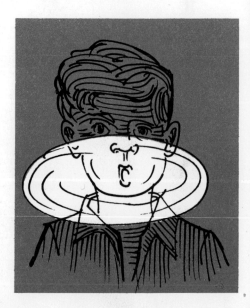

Double Trouble

Double bubble gum gives double bubble trouble.

Shut Up Shutter

A woman to her son did utter:
Go, my son, and shut the shutter.
The shutter's shut, the son did utter:
I cannot shut it any shutter.

There's no need to light a night light
On a light night like tonight;
For a night light's a slight light
On a bright night like tonight.

My dame hath a lame tame crane,
My dame hath a crane that is lame.

27

A Score of Sores

The preyful princess pierced and prick'd
    a pretty pleasing pricket;
Some say a sore; but not a sore,
    till now made sore with shooting.
The dogs did yell: put L to sore,
    then sorel jumps from thicket;
Or pricket sore, or else sorel;
    the people fall a-hooting.
If sore be sore, then L to sore
    makes fifty sores one sorel.
Of one sore I an hundred make
    by adding but one more L.

Moses supposes his toeses are roses,
But Moses supposes erroneously;
For nobody's toeses are posies of roses
As Moses supposes his toeses to be.

Sarah saw a shot-silk sash shop full of shot-silk sashes
as the sunshine shone on the side of the shot-silk sash shop.

Uncanny Granny

My grandmother sent me a new-fashioned three-cornered
   cambric country-cut handkerchief.
Not an old-fashioned three-cornered cambric country-cut
   handkerchief.
A new-fashioned three-cornered cambric country-cut
   handkerchief.

The Bankrupt Promoter

Bill had a billboard. Bill also had a board bill.
The board bill bored Bill, so that Bill sold the billboard
to pay the board bill. After Bill
sold the billboard to pay the board bill, the board bill
no longer bored Bill. But though he had no board bill,
neither did he have his billboard!

Jail Tale

Hipsters who swindle spinsters and clip tipsters
    who've tripped them risk being briskly frisked.
Such craven crooks, craning their necks,
    get cricks, catching a glimpse of cops.
Notable constables nab these nimble numskulls neatly,
    helping them, handily handcuffed and hobbled,
    to the hoosegow.

Don't pamper damp scamp tramps that camp under ramp lamps.

T Time

Thomas a Tattamus took two T's,
To tie two tups to two tall trees;
To frighten the terrible Thomas a Tattamus,
Tell me how many T's there are in all that.

Adolescent Present

*Ruby Rugby's brother bought and brought her
back some rubber baby-buggy bumpers.*

U Who

Dull humdrum murmurs lull, but hubbub stuns.
Lucullus snuffs no musk, mundungus shuns.
Puss purrs, buds burst, bucks butt, luck turns up trumps.
But full cups, hurtful, spur up unjust thumps.

Jack's Lacks

Jack Fletch can't fetch flints or filch perch.
He can't sketch ketches or scratch matches.
He can't thatch hutches or patch hatches.
Jack Fletch's a wretch.

Watchers of the Night

We supply watchmen to watch men you want watched.
We supply watchwatchmen to watch watchmen
    watching men you want watched.
We supply watchwomen to watch watchwatchmen
    watching watchmen watching men you want watched.
We supply wristwatches for witchwatchers
    watching witches Washington wishes watched.

The Sink, Swim or Skim Instinct

A male whale can have a whale of a sail.
But hale snails, quail and nightingales ail
To no avail and fail in gales.

Little Bigger Beggar

Mrs. Biggar had a baby. Which was the bigger?
The baby was a little Biggar! Which was the bigger,
Mrs. Biggar or the baby?
Mr. Biggar was the father Biggar!
Was the baby then bigger than Mrs. Biggar or Mr. Biggar?

Counting Rhymes

Intra, mintra, cutra, corn,
Apple seed and brier thorn;
Brier, wire, limber, lock,
Three geese in a flock.
One flew east and one flew west,
And one flew over the cuckoo's nest.

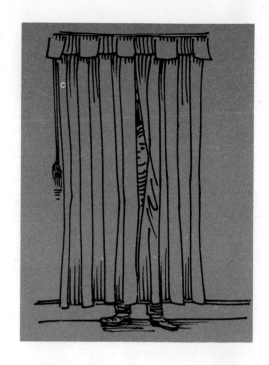

Ana, mana, mona, mike;
Barcelona, bona, strike;
Care, ware, frow, frack;
Hallico, ballico, wee, wo, wack!

Eni, bene, dunke, funke,
Rabe, schnabe, dippe, dappe,
Kase, knappe,
Ulle bulle nos
Ab ab aus;
Du liegst draus.

Vizzery, vazzery, vozery-vem,
Tizzery, tazzery, tozery-tem,
Hiram, jiram, cockrem, spirem,
Poplar, rollin, gem.

Haulk 'em, baulk 'em,
Mine corkum,
Hellicum, bellicum, buz,
Hytum, pytum, peni, pye,
Populorum, giggum, jye,
Stand the rot bye.

Keetum, peetum, peeny pie,
Populorum, gingum gie,
East, West, North, South,
Kirby, Kendal, cock him out.

One-ery, two-ery, hickory hum,
Fillison, follison, Nicholas, John,
Queever, quaver, Irish Mary,
Stenkarum, stankarum, buck!

Haley, maley, tippety fig,
Tiney, toney, tombo, nig;
Goat, throat, country note,
Tiney, toney, tiz.

The Mouse's Tail

say quickly...

> *The cat and the mouse*
> *Play'd in the malt-house:*

The cat bit the mouse's tail off. Pray, Puss, give me
my tail. No, says the cat, I'll not give you your tail,
till you go to the cow and fetch me some milk:

> *First she leapt, and then she ran,*
> *Till she came to the cow, and thus began:*

Pray, Cow, give me milk, that I may give cat milk,
that cat may give me my own tail again. No, said the cow,
I will give you no milk, till you go to the farmer
and get me some hay.

> *First she leapt, and then she ran,*
> *Till she came to the farmer, and thus began:*

Pray, Farmer, give me hay, that I may give cow hay,
that cow may give me milk, that I may give cat milk,
that cat may give me my own tail again. No, says the farmer,
I'll give you no hay, till you go to the butcher
and fetch me some meat.

38

First she leapt, and then she ran,
Till she came to the butcher, and thus began:
Pray, Butcher, give me meat, that I may give farmer meat,
that farmer may give me hay, that I may give cow hay,
that cow may give me milk, that I may give cat milk,
that cat may give me my own tail again. No, says the butcher,
I'll give you no meat, till you go to the baker
and fetch me some bread.

First she leapt, and then she ran,
Till she came to the baker, and thus began:
Pray, Baker, give me bread, that I may give butcher bread,
that butcher may give me meat, that I may give farmer meat,
that farmer may give me hay, that I may give cow hay,
that cow may give me milk, that I may give cat milk,
that cat may give me my own tail again.

Yes, says the baker, I'll give you some bread,
But if you eat my meal, I'll cut off your head.
Then the baker gave mouse bread, and mouse gave butcher bread,
and butcher gave mouse meat, and mouse gave farmer meat,
and farmer gave mouse hay, and mouse gave cow hay,
and cow gave mouse milk, and mouse gave cat milk,
and cat gave mouse her own tail again!

The Bittern Backbiter

A bitter biting bittern
Bit a better brother bittern,
And the bitter better bittern
Bit the bitter biter back.
And the bitter bittern, bitten,
By the better bitten bittern,
Said: "I'm a bitter biter bit, alack!"

Lost In the Maine Woods

The guide was guiding a guy.
As the guide guided the guy,
the guide guyed the guy,
until the guy would no longer be guided by a guide,
whom he had hired not to guy but to guide.
So the guyed guy guyed the guide.

Overdue IOU

Your Bob owes our Bob a bob.
If your Bob doesn't give our Bob
the bob your Bob owes our Bob,
our Bob will give your Bob a bob in the eye.

Oyster Stew Residue

She sells seashells by the seashore.
The shells she sells are surely seashells.
So if she sells shells on the seashore,
I'm sure she sells seashore shells.

Rich Bridget's midget digits itch.
Bridget's digits twitch.
If she fidgets with her digits,
Bridget's britches will be switched.

Longfellow Foreshortened

He killed the noble Mudjokivis,
With the skin he made the mittens,
Made them with the fur side inside,
Made them with the skin side outside;
He, to get the warm side inside,
Put the inside skin side outside:
He, to get the cold side outside,
Put the warm side fur side inside:
That's why he put the fur side inside,
Why he put the skin side outside,
Why he turned them inside outside.

Shiftless Sheep

Silly Sally swiftly shooed seven silly sheep.
The seven silly sheep Silly Sally shooed
shilly-shallied south.
These sheep shouldn't sleep in a shack;
sheep should sleep in a shed.

Neither Rain nor Snow

Scotch Paul Potts pays no postage.
He pitches pennies in the post office,
which for paying postage is.
Public properties are not spots
for penny-pinching, penny-pitching Scots.

Fish Dish

Kidnapped kippers caught by kindly skippers
Can't complain or flip their flippers.
Cut up, cooked and crisply fried,
Kippers can't kick when catsup's applied.

In fir tar is,
In oak none is,
In mud eel is,
In clay none is.
Goat eat ivy,
Mares eat oats.

Not In the Mud, Robert

Robert Rowley rolled a round roll 'round,
A round roll Robert Rowley rolled 'round;
Where rolled the round roll
Robert Rowley rolled 'round?

I saw a pair of peers,
sitting on a pair of piers,
paring a pair of pears.

Warning

Theophilus Thistledown,
    the successful thistle sifter,
in sifting a sieve of unsifted thistles,
thrust three thousand thistles
through the thick of his thumb.
If, then, Theophilus Thistledown,
    the successful thistle sifter,
in sifting a sieve of unsifted thistles,
thrust three thousand thistles
through the thick of his thumb,
see that thou, in sifting a sieve of unsifted thistles,
do not get the unsifted thistles stuck in thy tongue.

44

It is pilly-po-doddle and aligobung
    When the lollypop covers the ground;
Yet the poldiddle perishes plunkety-pung
    When the heart jimmy-coggles around.
If the soul cannot snoop at the gigglesome cart,
    Seeking surcease in gluggety-glug,
It is useless to say to the pulsating heart,
    "Yanky-doddle ker-chuggety-chug!"

Hutch Thatch

A thatcher of Thatchwood went to
    Thatchet a-thatching.
Did a thatcher of Thatchwood go to
    Thatchet a-thatching?
If a Thatcher of Thatchwood went
    to Thatchet a-thatching,
Where's the thatching the thatcher
    of Thatchwood had thatched?

A Child's Garden of Terse

When the breeze from the bluebottle's blustering blim
    Twirls the toads in a tooroomaloo,
And the whiskery whine of the wheedlesome whim
    Drowns the roll of the rattatattoo,
Then I dream in the shade of shally-go-shee,
    And the voice of the bally-molay
Brings the smell of stale poppy-cods blummered in blee
    From the willy-wad over the way.

Ah, the shuddering shoo and blinketty-blanks
    When the yungalung falls from the bough
In the blast of a hurricane's hicketty-hanks
    On the hills of the hocketty-how!
Give the rigamarole to the clangery-whang,
    If they care for such fiddledeedee;
But the thingumbob kiss of the whangery-bang
    Keeps the higgledy-piggle for me.

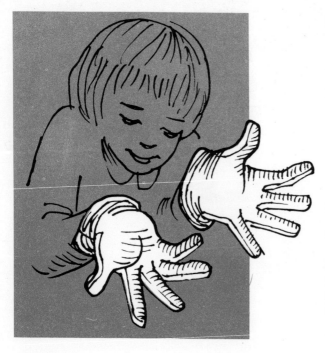

Left's Right

Ofttimes when I put on my gloves
I wonder if I'm sane,
For when I put the right one on
The right seems to remain
To be put on—that is, 'tis left;
Yet if the left I don
The other one is left and then
I have the right one on;
But still I have the left on right,
The right one, though, is left
To go right on the left right hand:
All right, if I am deft.

Sue Shuns Shoe Shock

Susan shineth shoes and socks;
socks and shoes shines Susan.
She ceased shining shoes and socks,
for shoes and socks shock Susan.

Strict strong stringy Stephen Stretch
slickly snared six sickly silky snakes.

A Kid, a Kid

say quickly...

A kid, a kid, my father bought
For two pieces of money:
    A kid, a kid.

Then came the cat, and ate
    the kid,
That my father bought
For two pieces of money:
    A kid, a kid.

Then came the dog, and bit
    the cat,
That ate the kid,
That my father bought
For two pieces of money:
    A kid, a kid.

Then came the staff, and
    beat the dog,
That bit the cat,
That ate the kid,
That my father bought
For two pieces of money:
    A kid, a kid.

Then came the fire, and
    burned the staff,
That beat the dog,
That bit the cat,
That ate the kid,
That my father bought
For two pieces of money:
    A kid, a kid.

Then came the water, and
    quenched the fire,
That burned the staff,
That beat the dog,
That bit the cat,
That ate the kid,
That my father bought
For two pieces of money:
    A kid, a kid.

Then came the ox, and
    drank the water,
That quenched the fire,
That burned the staff,
That beat the dog,
That bit the cat,
That ate the kid,
That my father bought
For two pieces of money:
    A kid, a kid.

Then came the butcher, and
    slew the ox,
That drank the water,
That quenched the fire,
That burned the staff,
That beat the dog,
That bit the cat,
That ate the kid,
That my father bought
For two pieces of money:
    A kid, a kid.

Then came the angel of death,
    and killed the butcher,
That slew the ox,
That drank the water,
That quenched the fire,
That burned the staff,
That beat the dog,
That bit the cat,
That ate the kid,
That my father bought
For two pieces of money:
    A kid, a kid.

Then came the Holy One,
    blessed be He!
And killed the angel of
    death,
That killed the butcher,
That slew the ox,
That drank the water,
That quenched the fire,
That burned the staff,
That beat the dog,
That bit the cat,
That ate the kid,
That my father bought
For two pieces of money:
    A kid, a kid.

Advice

Running amok, carrying rucksacks piggyback
Smack into haystacks, makes heads crack.

Cribbed Squibs

Pure fools rebuke furry mules,
purely for feeding on poor food,
while wits twit Schmitz who sits and knits slit skirts.
Yet glib drips dare to rib Gibbs, who, dipping his nib,
quibbles ad lib in script.

Look Out

He who knows not and knows not that he knows not,
    he is a fool, shun him.
He who knows not and knows that he knows not,
    he is simple, teach him.
He who knows and knows not that he knows,
    he is asleep, wake him.
He who knows and knows that he knows,
    he is wise, follow him.

Don't play hopscotch with top-notch watch fobs.

Mashed Hash

A singing hash slinger mixed fresh potato fritters
For five famished, mud-spattered, sewage pipe fitters.
Said the foolish pipe fitters to the flippant fritter slinger:
"Stick to your spud mixing. You're no opera singer."
But the mud-spattered pipe fitters were too rash.
The fritter-slinging singer fixed their hash.
'Midst splashing mash-mix the rash fitters dashed and fled,
Wishing they'd kept their mouths shut, except when fed.

A canner, exceedingly canny,
One morning remarked to his granny,
 "A canner can can
  Anything that he can;
But a canner can't can a can, can he?"

Escape Escapade

A fly and a flea flew up a flue.
Said the flea, "What shall we do?"
Said the fly, "Let us flee!"
Said the flea, "Let us fly!"
So they flew through a flaw in the flue.

I cannot bear to see a bear
Bear down upon a hare.
When bare of hair he strips the hare,
Right there I cry, "Forbear!"

Cruel Duel

Schott and Willing did engage
　　In duel fierce and hot;
Schott shot Willing willingly,
　　And Willing he shot Schott.

The shot Schott shot made Willing quite
　　A spectacle to see.
While Willing's willing shot went right
　　Through Schott's anatomy.

Russian Tongue Twister

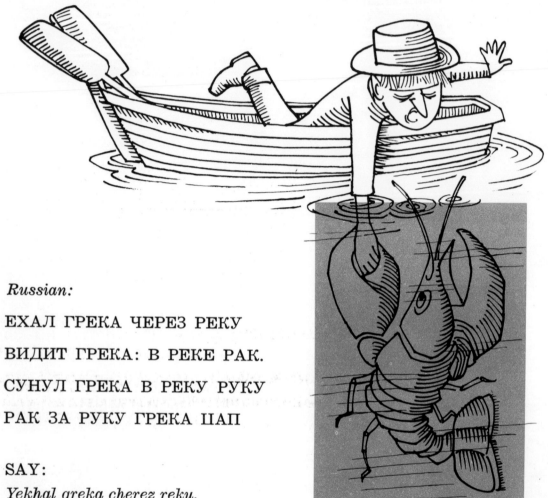

Russian:

ЕХАЛ ГРЕКА ЧЕРЕЗ РЕКУ

ВИДИТ ГРЕКА: В РЕКЕ РАК.

СУНУЛ ГРЕКА В РЕКУ РУКУ

РАК ЗА РУКУ ГРЕКА ЦАП

SAY:
Yekhal greka cherez reku.
Vidit greka v reke rak.
Sunul greka v reku ruku.
Rak za ruku greka tsap.

English:
A Greek ferried over a river.
The Greek saw a crayfish in the river.
The Greek reached with his hand into the river.
The crayfish grabbed the Greek by the hand.

54

Dutch Tongue Twister

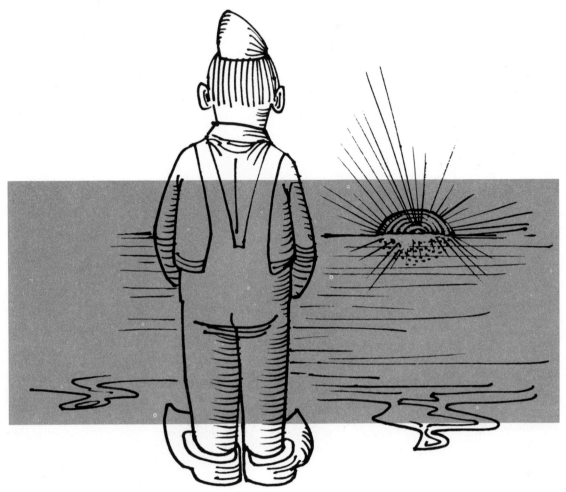

Dutch:

Ik zag de zon in de Zuiderzee zinken.

Hoor de kleine klompjes klepperen op de klinkers.

SAY:

Ick tzach de tzon in de tzidertzay tzinken.

Hoarr de klaine klompe-yus klepper'n op de klinkers.

English:

I saw the sun sink in the Zuiderzee.

I hear the little wooden shoes clip-clop on the cobblestones.

Chinese Tongue Twisters

壁上掛面鼓、
鼓上辦老虎、
老虎抓破了鼓、
買塊布來補。
不知道是布補鼓？
還是補虎？

流行：浙江鄞縣、紹興

壁上掛面鼓

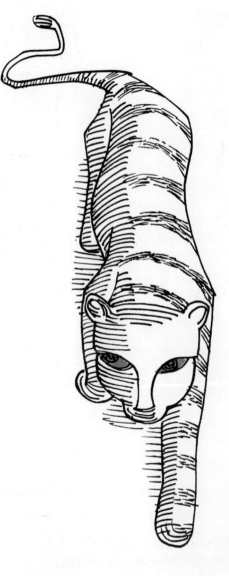

SAY:

Pi shang kua mien ku,
Ku shang hua lao hu,
Lao hu chua p'o liao ku,
Mai kuai pu lai pu,
Pu chih tao shih pu pu ku?
Huan shih pu pu hu?

English:
Upon the wall there hangs a drum;
upon the drum there's drawn a tiger,
Should the tiger claw the drum,
I'd buy cloth to mend it.
But would the cloth mend the drum?
Or would the cloth mend the tiger?

56

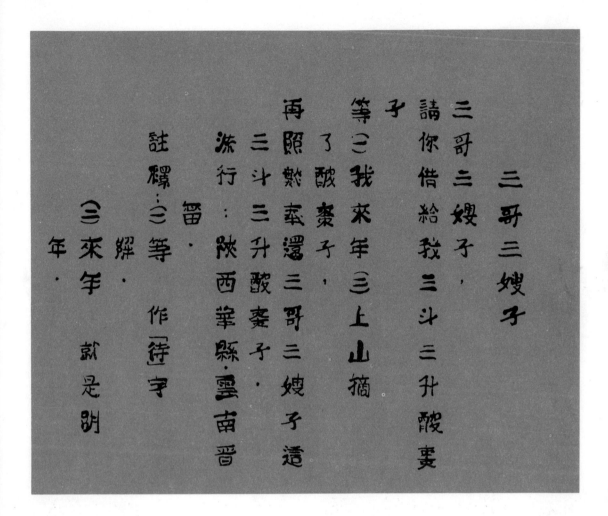

三哥三嫂子

三哥三嫂子，
請你借給我三斗三升酸棗
子〔一〕
等〔二〕我來年〔三〕上山摘。
了酸棗子，
再照數奉還三哥三嫂子這
三斗三升酸棗子。

流行：陝西華縣．雲南晉
留．

註釋：〔一〕等　作「待」字
解．〔二〕來年　就是明
年．

SAY:

San ko san sao tzu,

Ch'ing ni chieh chi ngo san tou san sheng suan tsao tzu,

Teng ngo lai nien shang shan che liao suan tsao tzu,

Tsai chao shu feng huan san ko san sao tzu che

San tou san sheng suan tsao tzu.

English:

Third brother and third brother's wife,

please lend me three pecks and three pints of sour dates.

Next year I'll climb the mountains to pluck sour dates,

to return third brother's and third brother's wife's

three pecks and three pints of sour dates.

French Tongue Twisters

French:

Un chasseur sachant chasser chassait sans son chien de chasse.

SAY:

Unn shassewr sashahn shassay shassay sahn sawn shyawn d'shahss.

English:

A hunter, knowing how to hunt, hunted without his hunting dog.

French:

Ton thé, t'a-t-il ôté ta toux?

SAY:

Tawn tay, tah teel otay tah too?

English:

Your tea, did it take away your cough?

French:

Étant sorti sans parapluie, il m'eût plus plu qu'il plût plus tôt.

SAY:

Aytahn sortie sahn para-plew-ee, eel m'yew plew plew keel plew plew toe.

English:

As I had gone out without an umbrella,

it would have pleased me more had it rained sooner.

About Tongue Twisters

The question of who wrote which of many of the Tongue Twisters and lip-tripping Double Talk in this book is shrouded in mystery as great as that of who composes the sayings found in Chinese Fortune Cookies. Some of the oldest may once have been political and satirical ditties, their original meaning long since lost. Others are said to have been mystic and magical incantations that accompanied the stirring of witches' brew. But certainly most were made up just for the fun of the thing, and passed from generation to generation.

Tongue Twisters have been seriously used at different times and places to test applicants for radio announcers' jobs, as sobriety checks, as hiccough cures and as supposed remedies for stutterers. But in any language their main purpose is, as it has always been: "to get your tang all tongueled up."*

"Peter Piper's Practical Principles of Plain and Perfect Pronunciation" is probably the oldest printed book of Twisters in the English language. Pictures and Twisters on the end-papers of this book are taken from the first American edition of 1830, and the first page is the introduction to the original British edition.

*Evan Esar: *The Humor of Humor*

Double Talk is not quite so old. It first became popular during the last half of the nineteenth century, part of a revived interest in nonsense poetry at the time of the birth of the limerick. Double Talk is really a practical joke in words. The object is to intersperse likely-sounding, yet meaningless, verbs, adjectives and nouns among meaningful words, so that the listener is never quite sure whether he is hearing sense or nonsense. While not defined as such, children's counting rhymes are earlier examples of Double Talk. They mean nothing—but the child who does the counting must sound as though he meant it. The only thing that does count is the last line . . . "you are it." And that is still the objective of Double Talk.

In our day, much of the word-of-mouth hand-me-down from child to child has been interrupted by TV, comics and other passive sport. Too many children and adults now imagine play as being possible only with things. I dedicate this book to the revival of play with sounds, words and ideas. This sort of verse and play with words is the stuff of which Mother Goose is made. In the tradition of this magical lore of childhood, I have assembled here the best I could find of the old and new, and have added a few of my own. I hope that all of these will be carried forward in the hearts of the children of today, to be repeated by them, when they walk and burp the babies of tomorrow.

Arnold Arnold

Index to First Lines

Mm

Matthew Mendleggs miss'd a
    meddling Monkey:
Did Matthew Mendleggs miss a
    meddling Monkey?
If Matthew Mendleggs miss'd a
    meddling Monkey,
Where is the meddling Monkey that
    Matthew Mendleggs miss'd?

Nn

Needy Noodle nipp'd his Neighbor's
    Nutmegs.
Did Needy Noodle nip his
    Neighbor's Nutmegs?
If Needy Noodle nipped his
    Neighbor's Nutmegs,
Where are his Neighbor's Nutmegs
    that Needy Noodle nipped?

Qq

Quixote Quicksight quiz'd a
    queerish Quidbox:
Did Quixote Quicksight quiz a
    queerish Quidbox?
If Quixote Quicksight quiz'd a
    queerish Quidbox,
Where's the queerish Quidbox
    Quixote Quicksight quiz'd?

Rr

Rory Rumpus rode a rawboned
    Racer:
Did Rory Rumpus ride a
    rawboned Racer?
If Rory Rumpus rode a rawboned
    Racer,
Where's the rawboned Racer
    Rory Rumpus rode?

Uu

Uncle's Usher urg'd an
    ugly Urchin:
Did Uncle's Usher urge an
    ugly Urchin?
If Uncle's Usher urg'd an
    ugly Urchin,
Where's the ugly Urchin Uncle's
    Usher urg'd?

Vv

Villiam Veedon vip'd his Vig
    and Vaistcoat:
Did Villiam Veedon vipe his Vig
    and Vaistcoat?
If Villiam Veedon vip'd his Vig
    and Vaistcoat,
Where are the Vig and Vaistcoat
    Villiam Veedon vip'd?

Oo

Oliver Oglethorpe ogled an Owl
    and Oyster;
Did Oliver Oglethorpe ogle an Owl
    and Oyster?
If Oliver Oglethorpe ogled an Owl
    and Oyster,
Where are the Owl and Oyster
    Oliver Oglethorpe ogled?

Pp

Peter Piper pick'd a Peck of
    Pickled Peppers:
Did Peter Piper pick a Peck of
    Pickled Peppers?
If Peter Piper pick'd a Peck of
    Pickled Peppers,
Where's the Peck of Pickled
    Peppers Peter Piper pick'd?

Ss

Sammy Smellie smelt a Smell
    of Smallcoal:
Did Sammy Smellie smell a Smell
    of Smallcoal?
If Sammy Smellie smelt a Smell
    of Smallcoal,
Where's the Smell of Smallcoal
    Sammy Smellie smelt?

Tt

Tip-Toe Tommy turn'd a Turk
    for Two-pence:
Did Tip-Toe Tommy turn a Turk
    for Two-pence?
If Tip-Toe Tommy turn'd a Turk
    for Two-pence,
Where's the Turk for Two-pence
    Tip-Toe Tommy turn'd?

Vw

Walter Waddle won a walking
    Wager:
Did Walter Waddle win a walking
    Wager?
If Walter Waddle won a walking
    Wager,
Where's the walking Wager
    Walter Waddle Won?

Xx Yy Zz

X Y Z have made my Brains
    to crack-o,
X smokes, Y snuffs, and Z
    chews tobacco;
Yet oft by X Y Z much learning's
    taught;
But Peter Piper beats them all
    to naught.